A DREAM DEFINED

A workbook for visionaries on a journey
toward making their dreams a reality

CHIANA J. SHIPP

To my beautiful daughter, you have inspired me more than you'll ever know. Your existence has pushed me to reach for new heights. It is because of you that I have grown to be the woman I am today.

Thank you, my dream girl.

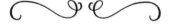

Table of Contents

Just one *dream defined* can ultimately

CHANGE YOUR LIFE

— CHIANA

This workbook belongs to...

Name: Natasha Vere / Nidia - 11/21/18
GIFT FROM   Palencia

Date: 9/5/18

This book is for you.
Wherever you are in your life, wherever you dream to be!

Introduction

Thank you so much for taking the first step toward making your dreams a priority. I can't begin to describe how elated I am that you have decided to embark on this journey toward making your dreams a reality.

Over the years, I have encountered so many different people, from many different walks of life. Talented, ambitious, hungry individuals with some pretty big dreams! I love meeting new people and picking their brains about their aspirations.

I knew from a young age that I wanted to help people reach their potential. In 2005, I worked a teen summer job through a program run by my hometown. Every week, we would have what were called " Personal Development Fridays." We would meet up in a conference room and hear a lecture from a life coach.

Can you imagine a room full of 15-year-olds, working just to buy the latest tennis shoes, being forced to listen to lectures from some boring life coach? One third of our group only showed up for the free lunch, another third fell asleep, and the last bit of us actually cared to listen. We would go over all sorts of material from resume building, to interviewing skills, even how to find an apartment!

While some people were pleased to be learning, I was focused on the life coach. "I want to do what she does," is what I would say to myself after each session. I studied her delivery and her approach and from that moment I knew my mission in life would be to help others flourish. When she gave us worksheets, I'd make copies and give them to my friends. I wanted to spread this knowledge around. I believe this is where I learned my first lesson about people and their dreams.

Most people have grand dreams but don't want to do anything to make them come true, or they simply don't know where to begin. Over time, I mastered many of the skills we were taught on these Fridays and before you know it, I was the go-to girl for everything! The moment my friends needed a resume, help with a job application, help with finding a place to live, I mean you name it! I was their girl. I'm almost certain I could have started some type of service business back then with all the favors I was doing. I even went as far as emailing the life coach after summer had ended asking her if she needed an intern or help because I really wanted to learn the industry. Let's just say, I don't think she was very fond of bringing a 15-year-old on her staff at that time.

I went on to graduate high school and I worked several random jobs. Every job I worked taught me the same lesson about myself and that was that I didn't want to work for anyone! It just was not for me! I was the kid making lemonade stands, posting flyers for my housecleaning service, making bracelets and selling them, I had a full candy store in my backpack by the time I hit middle school. The entrepreneurial spirit had always been in me from my grade school days.

I've always been a very crafty and creative girl, which led me to fall in love with event planning. I would plan events just to be able to organize them and hand-craft everything. It was very satisfying for me. Oh and having my baby girl in 2008 just gave me more of a reason to throw outlandish events. I gained a little popularity, but to my surprise, no one wanted to pay! Go figure. I would plan events for free just because I enjoyed it but over time it began to wear me down.

I had to really dig into the core desires of my heart and figure out how I could turn my dreams into a paycheck. I was always pretty good with outlining my goals and dreams. I always made vision boards and goal checklists. I managed to keep myself on track the majority of the time.

In 2015, I received an invite to a vision board workshop. I brought along my closest girlfriends and we had a good ol' goal-setting time! The following year we were not able to find a similar workshop so we had our own right in the living room! Of course, I put my event planning skills to use and made it the fanciest living room vision board party! My goal for that year was to find a way I could be a help to others.

That's when the idea hit me! I could carry on with these parties, and make them bigger and bigger! That way I am killing two birds with one stone. I am able to fulfill my desire to put on events and I could help others. It was a no-brainer!

repeat after me

I only attract loving people into my world.

Why I Chose to Start Sip & Dream

Year 2017, I launched Sip & Dream, Incorporated and held my very first vision board party. I chose to call it Sip & Dream because I wanted to make goal setting fun and exciting. I didn't want the standard workshop vibe. Instead, grab a glass of wine, and if you don't drink alcohol, have a virgin cocktail or even some coffee! Let's get acquainted and really dig into those dreams!

It was a total hit and the reviews were overwhelmingly great! For the first time ever, I knew I had figured it out! I had identified my dream and put the action behind making that dream a reality!

Now, let me help you! I designed this workbook to take you through the many phases of your life. You will be able to address where you are, identify where you want to go, and create a plan of action toward getting you there! As I mentioned previously, some people just simply need a little help and direction. The exercises in this workbook were created to serve as a map for outlining your wildest dreams.

repeat after me
Today will be better than yesterday and tomorrow will be better than today.

A Dream Defined Book Was Born

I'm sure you're wondering why you should pay attention to anything written in this book. I'll be the first to tell you, I am not some self-help guru who has life all figured out. Furthermore, I don't have a fancy psychology degree or certification... yet. What I do have is a burning desire to see people accomplish their dreams. I want to see everyone succeed!

Of course, simply telling you that won't do much. I mean, inviting you to one of my workshops will certainly help you out a great deal, but those two things alone will not suffice. You need a powerful resource that is always accessible.

The first thing I did when creating my vision board workshops was make a goal-setting pamphlet for the attendees. I knew that while the information they would receive for the workshop would be helpful, they would benefit most by being able to have the material at hand.

Thus, A Dream Defined Book was born. I sat down day after day, writing and thinking of ways to really guide you through every part of fulfilling your dreams. This book is filled with real-life stories and thought provoking exercises. My dream is to help, to guide, and to lead as many people as I can to victory. This workbook is my way of taking your hand and helping you along your journey. My hope is that somewhere between these pages you will find yourself and more importantly, realize that having a dream is one thing, but having your dream defined can change your life.

Here's How I Want You to Use This Workbook

Take your time! There is no need to rush. This is a marathon, not a sprint. In order to be clear and concise, you cannot be rushed.

Just let your heart flow! There is no need to strive for perfection during this process. Write out exactly what is on your heart and make your adjustments along the way.

Honesty is the best policy! This book does not come with a set of judges. These exercises won't do you any good if you are lying to yourself. You have to be real with yourself before you will be able to see anything change.

This workbook will serve as your starting point and reference point. It's nice to be able to come back and check in on how far you have come. Read your responses periodically. Stay on course but most importantly have fun! I want you to turn through these pages and get excited about your future. Add stickers, pictures, drawings, whatever you deem necessary to the pages. You will come across exercises that will ignite your thoughts. I want you to dig as deep as you can into the core desires of your heart. Use this as a guideline to jumpstart your vision board. After you figure out what your vision is (in writing), I want you to make it plain (with photos).

In true Sip & Dream fashion, grab your drink of choice, whether it be an alcoholic beverage or a cold glass of ice tea. Pick out your favorite glass, dedicate some time to be alone, and let's get your vision out on paper.

This is YOUR workbook. Make it personal and take it personal.

Seeing is believing!

When you believe it, you can achieve it!

Grab your pen and let's get started!

repeat after me

I have both strengths and weaknesses. I concentrate on my strengths and on improving my weaknesses.

Let the Dreaming Begin

Throughout this book you will find some of my favorite quotes. I truly believe one good quote a day can keep the negative thoughts at bay.

You will also come across affirmations labeled "Repeat After Me." Stop what you're doing at that very moment and read the affirmation aloud.

These tokens are put in place to help shift your mindset. Speak greatness into your life with positive quotes and positive affirmations!

repeat after me

I am a money magnet. I welcome prosperity and abundance to overflow in my life.

Reflect

It's a risk, but I believe the best investment you can make in anything is in yourself.

INVEST IN YOURSELF

and then back it up.

Back it up with what you do.

— IMAN

Honesty Hour

Let's take a moment to reflect on the progress you made in the previous year.

What goals did you set last year that you were able to accomplish?

_____

_____

_____

_____

_____

_____

Were you able to make any progress toward a major goal that you are still striving to accomplish today?

_____

_____

_____

_____

_____

_____

What are you committed to doing this year that you spent all of last year putting off?

_____
_____
_____
_____
_____
_____
_____
_____

What is one key thing you can do differently to be certain none of your dreams slip through your fingers?

_____
_____
_____
_____
_____
_____
_____
_____

You *don't* have to hold
YOURSELF HOSTAGE
to who you used to be.

— OPRAH WINFREY

Let's Get Real

Now, for the least fun part of this entire workbook. Let's take a look at your reality. This next exercise will help you to address where you are presently. The good, the bad, and the ugly. My hope is that we can tackle these areas early on and let this be the last time we have to address them. Just because this is your truth right now does not mean you are required to continue to live this reality. I need you to be as honest as possible about your current state. Some of you may be happy with where you are, while others want to run far away from their situations. The first step in getting where you want to be is understanding where you are and deciding you are not going to stay there.

where are you?

Mentally

Emotionally

Financially

Professionally

Spiritually

You become what you believe
Not what you wish for but what you truly believe, wherever you are in life.

LOOK AT YOUR BELIEFS

They put you there.

— OPRAH WINFREY

Get It Through Your Head

Your beliefs can be holding you back. It's time for a belief makeover!

You would not believe how many of us have been conditioned to live with limiting thoughts. It's almost as if from the moment we are born, we are programmed to believe life is a challenge.

Some of the popular phrases we were raised to believe are:

"Money doesn't grow on trees."

"Nothing happens in the blink of an eye."

"You have to go to college in order to amount to anything."

"It's better to play it safe."

"Slow and steady wins the race."

SAYS WHO? Who came up with this logic? I guarantee you it started with someone who was afraid, afraid to push boundaries and break barriers. I can tell you right now; no one has ever made any life-altering changes playing it safe.

Throw all of those beliefs that lock you in a box out the window. You have to take hold of your dreams and pursue them relentlessly, with everything you have until they manifest. If you really believe that you won't amount to anything unless you have a college degree, then that is a struggle you are choosing to live. You can make a decision right now to not conform to any beliefs instilled in you by fear. Believe that you are great; believe that money does in fact grow on trees and there is a plethora of it to go around the block a few times. Believe that everything you touch turns to gold. Once you change the way you view things, and start to believe life is not just a challenge but a beautiful journey, watch your life begin to change. If you sit up every day and believe that your bills are ruining your life, your bills will without a doubt ruin your life! Check your beliefs at the door and don't bring in any of that small-minded stuff with you! I dare you to only believe in success, beauty, power, abundance, peace, and love.

What is one limiting belief that you were raised up on that you would get rid of for good?

_____

_____

_____

_____

_____

_____

_____

repeat after me

I deserve to be compensated well for my skills and knowledge.

Keep Your Eyes On Your Own Paper

Comparison is the thief of joy! Everything is made to look glamorous these days and if you don't keep your focus on yourself, you will lose sight of where you are headed. People get sidetracked all day long. Scrolling through Instagram feeds and Facebook timelines all day. Do yourself a favor, log off!

No one else is you and that is your power. Spend your free time dwelling on how great you are and how great you dream of being.

It's easy to get caught up looking at how perfect and together everyone "appears" to be. Look at all these people appearing to be doing so great in life, look at all these luxury items they appear to have. Notice the emphasis on "appear!" 9 times out of 10, what they are displaying is not even their reality. Now here you are, letting what other people (appear) to have get you down. If all of your time were spent on building yourself up, you wouldn't even care about what others are doing because the transitions taking place in your life would be so satisfying. That's the mode I'm trying to push you into. Tunnel vision. Don't give away the precious time that could be spent bettering YOU beating yourself up because you are not where you think you should be based on where others are. Set your own bar and don't measure your success on anyone else's scale. This is your life and it is tailored specifically for you. Spend more time with your eyes on your paper, figuratively and literally.

I am guilty of this. I cannot sit here and act like I am above any of these antics because I've been there. I've been that girl! For a long time all I could think is "what am I doing wrong?" It took me some time to get it through my head and change. The only thing we are doing wrong is looking at the paper next to us. This is an elementary school lesson that needs to be applied to our adult life. We must have forgotten about the times we copied the person next to us in class, and failed! You are failing yourself in the same way every time you take your focus off of you. You are enough! Great things will begin to unfold for you when it is your time! In the meantime, keep pushing forward.

repeat after me

I am worthy of living out my grandest dreams.

Clarity

Your mind must arrive at the destination BEFORE YOUR LIFE DOES

— UNKNOWN

My Focus Word

Every year, I like to choose a focus word that will set the tone for everything I dream of the year being. When you reflect on the vision that you have for yourself, is there a word that comes to mind? What word will be your inspiration and motivation? Think of one word that will fuel you in the right direction and serve as a reminder. Some examples of words I've used in the past are growth, preparation, renew, and consistency.

My Focus Word Is:

I am choosing to focus on this word because:

My Dreams – The Breakdown

I'm happy to have that stuff out of the way. It's time we focus on the NOW. In the next exercise I want you to get detailed and break down your goals. There are eight subjects listed; push yourself to list a minimum of five specific goals under each subject. They don't have to be in any particular order; we will cross that bridge later in the workbook.

Family

repeat after me
Doors of opportunity are now open for me to fulfill my dreams.

Friends & Social Life

Love & Relationships

Health & Fitness

Spiritual & Wellness

Wealth & Finances

Career & Business

Travel

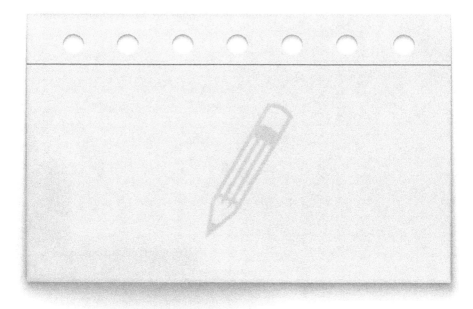

repeat after me

Everyday I am a better person. I am thriving and accomplishing my dreams at an astonishing pace.

Sometimes the only way to
win the game
is to
QUIT PLAYING

— CHIANA

✔ Check Yourself

What is my #1 Priority?

_____
_____
_____
_____
_____

What can instantly put me in a good mood?

_____
_____
_____
_____
_____
_____
_____

What can instantly put me in a bad mood?

What can I do to shift my mood when I feel myself falling into a negative space?

What new positive habits can I implement into my daily routine?

_____

_____

_____

_____

_____

_____

_____

_____

_____

What old negative habits can I rid myself of for good?

_____

_____

_____

_____

_____

_____

_____

_____

_____

What are a few ways I can make a positive impact on others?

At this moment, I am committed to making myself feel...?

What is one thing I can do well that can make a difference in my life as well as the lives of others?

_____
_____
_____
_____
_____
_____
_____
_____
_____
_____
_____
_____
_____
_____
_____
_____

repeat after me

I am financially free. Money is no longer an issue.

Make your

vision

so clear that your

FEARS

become irrelevant.

— UNKNOWN

Vision

It all starts with a vision

At the beginning of every year, people create vision boards displaying many of their dreams and goals. The problem with the typical vision board is that majority of people create these boards for aesthetics only with no real understanding of their purpose. Over the next few pages, I'll explain what a vision board is, and why you should create one.

repeat after me

Multiple streams of income is a constant in my life.

What Is a Vision Board?

Besides the obvious posterboard with magazine clippings, a vision board is a creative tool in which you use constant visualization to manifest your dreams. A vision board is one of the best ways to lay out the vision you have for your life collectively and be able to view it all in one place. Vividly. Sometimes it's better to dream in color.

Why is that so many people are constantly setting their sights on the same goals over and over? It's because they have yet to master the proper way to set specific goals and achieve them. Hopefully going over these easy guidelines will help you to create your most powerful vision board yet!

You have to be specific when it comes to setting goals!

I can tell you all day long that I want to be a doctor but does that mean it's automatically going to happen? NO! You have to get in the habit of breaking your goals down. When do you plan to do it? How do you plan to do it? Why do you want to do it? Once you are able to identify the basics, all that's left to do is put some action behind those goals.

The Three General Rules For Creating A Powerful Vision Board

1 *Be Specific* – Narrow your goals down to the minutest detail. You should be able to look at your goals and know exactly where you're headed and what you need to do to get there.

2 *Get Creative* – Magazines are not the only source for inspiration. Collect pictures and phrases that relate to your dreams from various places.

3 *Be Organized* – A scattered vision board is a sign of a scattered brain. Place your pictures in sequence as they connect with each other. For example, make a corner dedicated to places you plan to travel and make the opposite corner dedicated to finding love. Clean and clear!

repeat after me

My business is excelling more and more everyday!

Types Of Vision Boards

1 *Broad* – This board is made to cover a set of goals one might have that will take a few years to accomplish. It might touch on every aspect of life from traveling goals and starting a family to business plans. This board will usually display a person's life goals on a large scale.

2 *Timeline* – This type of board only focuses on goals to be accomplished within a certain time frame.

3 *Subject-Focused* – This type of board focuses on one particular subject, fitness for example. This board will display all the fitness goals one might have.

4 *Digital* – This new concept where you compile all your pictures onto a computer document and simply print it out onto paper.

repeat after me

I easily attract rewarding business opportunities.

What You Should Include On Your Vision Board

How many times have you sat around skimming through magazines, clipping catchy phrases and pretty pictures? Did you accomplish anything? Did you even have a plan? Let's stray away from that "scrapbook method" and learn to really lay out those dreams!

A visual representation of your dreams will not always be found browsing through countless magazines. We have to take the process a step further. You want to purchase a home? Go on Google and search for a picture of a home with a "SOLD" sign. Print the image and add it to your board. It's that simple. Again, it's about getting specific. You should even take it a step further and write a date on it. What day do you see yourself closing the deal on your home? Visualize it! Now, I'm not saying you should get rid of finding pictures in magazines completely. I want you to still do that. I just want to point out different ways to get specific with your vision.

Always keep your completed vision board where you can see it in plain sight. Frame it, tape it, or make it a fancy piece of artwork for your home. Go to whatever lengths necessary to make looking over your goals an everyday thing.

repeat after me

I deserve to be compensated well for my skills and knowledge.

If you don't get out of the **box you were raised in,** you won't understand

HOW MUCH BIGGER

the world is

— ANGELINA JOLIE

Inspiration

Recommended Reading

This is a list of some of my favorite books. These books have all helped me with my growth in one way or another. A good book can really give you a fresh perspective and new insight. Make it a goal to read more and feed your mind inspiring content. These are all gems that should be added to your home library.

✓ *Be Obsessed Or Be Average* – by Grant Cardone

✓ *You Are A Badass* – by Jen Sincero

✓ *You Can Heal Your Life* – by Louise Hay

✓ *Girl Code* – by Cara Alwill Leyba

✓ *Living Beyond Your Feelings* – by Joyce Meyer

✓ *Purpose Awakening* – by Tourè Roberts

✓ *The Go-Giver* – by Bob Burg

✓ *Think And Grow Rich* – by Napoleon Hill

✓ *The Power Of Habit* – by Charles Duhigg

✓ *Year of Yes* – by Shonda Rhimes

✓ *Do Yourself A Favor...Forgive!* – by Joyce Meyer

✓ *The Magic* – by Rhonda Byrne

✓ *Nice Girls Don't Get The Corner Office* – by Lois Frankel

✓ *The Five Love Languages* – by Gary Chapman

✓ *The Mastery Of Love* – by Don Miguel Ruiz

✓ *The Celestine Prophecy* – by James Redfield

✓ *The Seven Spiritual Laws Of Success* –
by Deepak Chopra

✓ *The Confident Woman Devotional* – by Joyce Meyer

✓ *The Alchemist* – by Paulo Coelho

✓ *Women Who Run With Wolves* –
by Clarissa Pinkola Estés

✓ *A New Earth: Awakening To Your Life's Purpose* –
by Eckhart Tolle

✓ *Start With Why* – by Simon Sinek

repeat after me

*I am a money magnet, I welcome prosperity and
abundance to overflow in my life.*

This Year I Will Read...

☐ 1 _____

☐ 2 _____

☐ 3 _____

☐ 4 _____

☐ 5 _____

☐ 6 _____

☐ 7 _____

☐ 8 _____

☐ 9 _____

☐ 10 _____

You can not teach a
man anything,
you can
only help him
FIND IT WITHIN
himself.
— GALILEO GALILEI

Positive Vibes Only

Staying positive during the course is a major key. Trials will always come but you don't have to allow them to destroy you. When you are getting close to winning, so many things will try to detour you off the route to success. Never fold! Kill your fears and doubts with positivity. Successful people all have successful habits. Check out the different ways you can make effective positive changes today.

Wake up earlier than usual to spend some time alone. Have your tea/coffee, meditate, do some stretches. Make it a point to spend time alone with your thoughts every day.

Don't forget to pray! Start each day with your prayers, goals, and affirmations. Look over your vision board. Visualize where you want to be routinely.

Clean up your networks. Remove all of the negative people and things that give you a reason to think negatively toward others. Unfollow accounts that cause you to gossip and compare.

Unsubscribe from junk email lists. Keep your inbox clear of sales, promotions, and any unnecessary information.

Get organized and keep clean spaces. Clean spaces promote clean thoughts. Nine times out of 10, if your living quarters are chaotic, so is your life. You can't think clearly surrounded by clutter. Organize that stack of mail, clean out your closets and your car, and keep up with your house chores.

Change your phone number. If you've had the same number for a very long time, change it! Everyone does not need access to you. Only stay connected to people who add value to your life.

Audible books are your friends. Turn off the radio sometimes and turn on a book! Find an inspiring podcast to listen to. You need to constantly feed your mind positive content. Music is great, but the wrong song can put a damper on your mood. Make a happy playlist of songs that make you feel good. I call it my feel good playlist. Turn off those depressing love songs and turn on something that's going to make you feel good.

Avoid being sucked into other people's problems. You don't even realize how much of a negative effect it has on you subconsciously. When people call you with drama, change the subject. Don't subject yourself to the negative energy of others. If you do, it will eventually translate into your life.

Stop talking about your problems. Period. No one likes a Negative Nancy! Talk to God or buy a journal. The people you are discussing your problems with don't care! The quickest way to stop giving life to your problems is to stop talking about them.

Talk about the good things happening instead. If good things aren't happening, talk about all the good things that are going to begin happening until they actually manifest.

Make a happy file! Start collecting texts, emails, and praises you receive that make you smile. Put pictures of things that make you smile; it could be a memory. Write down things that you've accomplished that you are proud of. When you are feeling down, pull out your happy file and look through it until your mood improves.

End your day with gratitude. Buy a notebook or journal specifically for giving thanks. Before you go to bed, list at least five things you are thankful for pertaining to your day.

Take yourself on a date. You must be able to enjoy your own company without anyone else around. Get dressed up and take yourself on a real date, I'm not kidding. You'll start to discover different things about yourself and the world around you.

Give yourself a break! Use one of your sick days that you never take and give yourself a day to unwind and rejuvenate. Hire that babysitter or housekeeper every now and again to take some of the load off of you. Life was not meant to be all work. Take some time to relax.

Beautify your environment. Add some fresh flowers to your home, splurge on that candle you love, get yourself a comforter that feels like you're sleeping in a 5-star hotel. Make everything around you beautiful!

Fall in love with taking care of yourself. Work out, start eating healthy, groom yourself regularly, and check in on your health.

repeat after me

I only attract loving people into my world.

Positive Vibes Checklist

10 positive habits that I will implement this year

☐ 1 _____

☐ 2 _____

☐ 3 _____

☐ 4 _____

☐ 5 _____

☐ 6 _____

☐ 7 _____

☐ 8 _____

☐ 9 _____

☐ 10 _____

He who is not *courageous* enough to take

RISKS

will accomplish *nothing* in life.

— MUHAMMED ALI

Perspective & Passion

Live A Life You Love

Are you ready for the toughest question of all? I say toughest because you only get one life. There are no redo's and no restart buttons given to us when we are born. We are only given one lifetime to get it right. Think about this question for a moment before you answer it.

How do you want to spend your one and only life?

_____

_____

_____

_____

_____

_____

_____

_____

_____

_____

_____

_____

_____

_____

_____

_____

If you were able to write an answer to that question, I am truly impressed! A lot of times, we spend our entire life searching for the answer. You might have an answer for that question today, and next year have an entirely new answer. It's really dependent on how you view your world at the moment. Perspective changes everything. Challenge yourself to develop a new perspective and take a stab at that question again.

Know without a doubt that you can have everything you've ever dreamed of. You are limitless. Your dream life is here for the taking! If you are still feeling stuck, that's OK! Let's dig a little deeper.

In a perfect world, my life is one that:

If I knew without a doubt that I could not fail, I would…?

My ideal life is one that allows me to…?

And again,

How do you want to spend your one and only life?

I hope you were able to get clear with your answers the second time around. Doesn't that feel good? I feel good knowing that you are making progress through these exercises.

Hobbies vs. Profitable Passion

During the introduction of this workbook, I briefly touched on a few of my many different hobbies. There is no shortage of things that I enjoy doing. I'm sure you can relate but just because we are good at something doesn't mean that is our calling. I really love to craft things but do people love to buy my crafts? Often times the answer is no.

Which one of your hobbies has the potential to be a profitable passion? A hobby is something you enjoy doing in your spare time for pleasure. A profitable passion is something you enjoy doing, something you are good at doing, which in turn can make you money! During this next exercise we will go over your hobbies. My hope is to identify what you are the best at, and what you can turn into a profitable passion!

repeat after me

I only attract loving people into my world.

Hobbies

I really enjoy doing this in my free time:

1

2

3

4

5

I can do this and not get bored:

1

2

3

4

5

repeat after me

I am worthy of living out my grandest dreams.

Profitable Passion

People always tell me I am so good at:

1

2

3

4

5

I am the go-to person in my circle for:

1

2

3

4

5

repeat after me

My business is excelling more and more everyday!

Look at both sets of answers. Do any of your hobbies relate to any of your profitable passion answers? Do any of them go hand in hand? Hopefully you have one or two things that connect! Those hobbies of yours that can translate into profitable passions are your starting point for making the things you are good at work for you financially.

repeat after me

I am financially free. Money is no longer an issue.

Miracles
start to happen
when you give as
much energy to your
dreams as you do
YOUR FEARS
— UNKNOWN

Manifest

There is Power in Your Pen

Something about writing things out in pen just makes things feel real. I leave home every day with a purse and a planner bag. People love to make fun of my planner bag because it's so big and heavy but it is truly my lifeline. My dreams are so big; they require their own space and bag. Inside my bag is a happy planner, my gratitude journal, a pen case, a blank journal, and a folder full of my random thoughts on scrap paper. This workbook started out as hundreds of pieces of scrap paper notes!

People can't seem to understand why I travel with all of these items when I have an iPhone. I know the iPhone is equipped with a calendar and the capability to write notes; it's just not the same as a good old pen and pad. Call me old-fashioned but my dreams feel tangible when I can look at them spread out in front of me, in my own handwriting. I don't trust technology that much to rely on my phone or computer to be the holder of my precious dreams. If you have been taking the new-school approach and using technology, switch it and write it out in pen. Get your thoughts out on paper, not in a cell phone!

I also have a whiteboard in my home that I write my goals on and look at frequently. Write out your dreams and get them out into the universe. You will be surprised how much more you will get done just by having a list to refer back to.

repeat after me

Everyday I am a better person. I am thriving and accomplishing my dreams at an astonishing pace.

When you write out
your dreams
you give them
the right to

COME TO LIFE

— CHIANA

21 Days of Gratitude

Studies show that it takes 21 days to form a new habit. I dare you to take my 21-Day Gratitude Challenge. Start out with writing down one thing you're thankful for every day and then add more as you get better at it. Each day, before you go to bed, stop and write out the things you are thankful for. These things can be big or small. For example, "Today I am thankful for sunshine!"

It's important to give thanks religiously; the universe will thank you in return. Learn to give thanks through the pretty times and the ugly times. Everything you experience is conditioning you for the next phase of your life. Try your best to keep an attitude of gratitude and watch the universe begin to reward you. When you wake up in the morning, before you even step out of bed, say THANK YOU! When you step in the shower and the warm water hits your skin, say THANK YOU! We are blessed beyond measure; the things we should be thankful for are endless. Be thankful for the little things and watch the bigger things unfold.

Someone once told me to pay my bills with thanks. I thought it was the craziest idea because come on; paying bills has always been a dreadful task. Well, I tried it out; every time I had a bill to pay I would say to myself, "I am so thankful I am able to cover this bill" or "I am so grateful that I have money to cover my expenses." The more I did it, the more I enjoyed paying my bills. It helped me to understand how powerful our words are!

If you're constantly complaining about the things that are kicking your butt, guess what? They will continue to. You don't allow new blessings to enter your life when you are ungrateful.

Give thanks! I've provided a chart for you. Commit to 21 Days of Gratitude. Each day, write out one thing you are grateful for. After you complete the challenge, take it a step further and buy a gratitude journal. Make writing gratitude lists a lifelong habit!

Today I Am Grateful For...

Day 1 _____

Day 2 _____

Day 3 _____

Day 4 _____

Day 5 _____

Day 6 _____

Day 7 _____

Day 8 _____

Day 9 _____

Day 10 _____

Day 11 _____

Day 12 _____

Day 13 _____

Day 14 _____

Day 15 _____

Day 16 _____

Day 17 _____

Day 18 _____

Day 19 _____

Day 20 _____

Day 21 _____

Purpose

Finding Your Why

As great as this all sounds, there will be days when you get discouraged. No one is programmed to be in a happy mood 24/7/365. On the days you find yourself needing a little reassurance, think about why you are doing this. Why is it so vital for you to see your dreams manifest? Nine years ago my "Why" changed completely. I lived a life all about Chiana until I had my first child. She became my "Why!" She is looking up to me, I am her greatest influence, and every decision I make, I make with her future in mind. I work so hard to provide a stable lifestyle for her. Here's an overview of how a typical day normally goes for me.

6:30 A.M.   Wake up, pack lunches, and make breakfast for Jaila.

8:00 A.M.   Deadline to have both of us dressed, fed, and out of the house.

8:15 A.M.   Drop Jaila off to school.

9:00 A.M.   Clock in for my work shift.

2:00 P.M.   Use my hour lunch break to run errands for my home and squeeze in food somewhere.

7:00 P.M.   Finally I'm off of work after 10 hours!

7:30 P.M.   Race to pick up Jaila, get home to get dinner started, homework finished, and baths all before 9:30!

After 9:30 P.M. If I am not dead tired, I may pick up a book or catch one of my favorite shows. Go to sleep, wake up, and do it all over again!

Le'Struggle!

Time for myself and time for my kid was pretty much non-existent. Here I am making fairly decent money but I had no freedom. I was losing touch with my daughter. The majority of my time was spent building someone else's dream.

To make matters worse, my mom was having health and financial troubles and the help I was able to offer her was pretty scarce.

I can recall when we experienced a horrific double homicide in my family and the one-year anniversary had come up. I went to my boss and told him I would need the day off to spend with my family because it was going to be a very difficult day. He told me he didn't know what to say because my coworker had already requested the day off and he couldn't say yes and have no front office coverage! Imagine my frustration. I knew at that very moment I didn't want to ever be in a position to have to ask for permission to take care of my personal needs. Everything changed for me that day. I work day and night on a plan to get myself out of the corporate rat race!

My daughter depends on it. My family depends on it, and MY SANITY depends on it!

Every time I get tired and feel like I want to give up, I just remember why I am doing this in the first place.

What is your reason why? What is the reason you won't allow yourself to fail?

It's the repitition of affirmations that leads to *belief* and once that belief becomes a deep conviction, THINGS BEGIN TO HAPPEN

— MUHAMMAD ALI

Affirm It

Self-love is the best love.

Summer of 2006, I enrolled in this big-time makeup artistry academy in Hollywood. I was fresh out of high school and had dreams of becoming a Film/TV makeup artist. The first course we were required to take was basic beauty makeup. I wasn't necessarily thrilled about taking this because I felt I could learn beauty tricks on YouTube somewhere. It was a requirement so I obliged.

First day of class, I show up ecstatic to embark on my new path. In walks our instructor, Ms. G. She had this eccentric vibe to her. She smelled like the finest essential oils and her presence alone was very demanding. I was interested in what this woman had to offer. Throughout our lessons she would preach about the power of affirmations, the power of your words, and the power of loving yourself! Her class felt more like a self-help seminar than a makeup class! I believe she shoved positivity down our throats so much we had no time to be negative.

I remember one day in particular, I was tired of doing all of those basic makeup looks. I was ready to learn how to transform people into Planet Of The Apes characters! I guess she could sense that I was frustrated because she pulled me to the side to talk. I went on and on about how I had to catch the train 60 miles every day just to practice foundation blending techniques on my classmates! It wasn't fulfilling. "I want to make the big money; THIS IS STUPID!" I said to her. She looked at me and said, "If you don't fix that negative attitude, you're going to always attract unfulfilling experiences in your life." She said, "I want you to buy this book and tell me what you think of it after you've read it."

The book was "You Can Heal Your Life" by Louise Hay. Every morning on my annoying train ride to school I read it. The life lessons I learned from that book were worth more than the ridiculously high-priced tuition I paid to attend that academy. I couldn't even put the book down. I told my friends and family about it and they thought I was being some weird universe freak. It's hard trying to get people with strong religious backgrounds on board with affirmations! That didn't stop me. This book changed everything for me. It was this book that helped me realize that the power had been mine the whole time! I would recite my affirmations during every train ride and declare to have a prosperous day. It helped me to keep the focus on loving myself even though I was not where I wanted to be.

Self-love is the best form of self-care. I would argue it to be the most effective! You can think yourself right into a state of depression and illness if you aren't careful. Comparing yourself to others and dwelling on your shortcomings and insecurities will always hinder you.

I knew that I had to make a change and love myself through every stage, every failure, and every part of my journey to success. Being negative about my life and the things I thought were working against me did not get me to the finish line any quicker. My mood improved tremendously and so did the opportunities in my life. Ironically, I went on to do beauty makeup on some popular TV sets and even worked as a manager for a top cosmetic line at Nordstrom.

I know what you're thinking, "but you hated the beauty makeup class!" I hated it because I was being negative, I was being impatient, and I didn't realize it was just a small piece of my amazing puzzle! What you speak over your life will eventually manifest. The power of the tongue is nothing to play with! If you want to see positive changes happen you have to speak positivity like it's your second language. Affirm it! I would recite these two affirmations from "You Can Heal Your Life" before class:

I love myself; therefore I work at a job I truly enjoy

doing, one that uses my creative talents and abilities,

working with and for people I love and who love me,

and earning a good income.

I love myself; therefore I live totally in the now,

experiencing each moment as good and knowing that

my future is bright and joyous and secure,

for I am a beloved child of the Universe

and the Universe lovingly takes care of me

now and forever more.

Sure enough, my future was brighter than ever before!

Self-love is deeper than only loving your outward appearance. It's also about loving yourself enough to know that you are worthy of life-changing opportunities. You are worthy of living a fulfilling life!

You. Are. Worth. It.

Find some affirmations you love and begin to recite them every hour. Here's how you can make good use of your cellphone. Use the reminder app and set a reminder to pop up every hour with your "Affirmation of the day." Do this daily with one powerful affirmation! Every time that reminder pops up on your screen, say the affirmation aloud!

Post-it notes will come in handy for this exercise too! I have post-it notes on the dashboard of my car, on my bed frame, on my mirrors, on my computer at work, all over the place! Put your affirmations in the places you look at the most. When you catch yourself being negative, fight off that negative energy with an affirmation. The affirmations that are used for the repeat after me segment of this workbook, use those! I added them for your benefit. Here are a few more of my go-to affirmations just to get the ball rolling!

- I love myself unconditionally and accept myself as I am.

- I am proud of myself and all that I have accomplished.

- I accept myself for what I am and I am constantly trying to better myself.

J. Cole said it best. "Love yourself girl or nobody will." You have the power to create your own beautiful world right within you. Love yourself enough to welcome amazing things. A negative spirit will only turn your rewards away.

We give so much of ourselves to others on a daily basis. It's time we start to pour a little extra love into our own love tanks! Stop beating yourself up over the inevitable and love, love, love yourself like your life depends on it because truth is, it does! Flaws, mistakes, and all! How much do you love yourself?

What is one thing you can do this year to focus on loving yourself a little more?

If you can
dream it
YOU CAN DO IT

— WALT DISNEY

Raising Children Who Dream Big

Imagine how far we would be in our lives today, if we grew up in a household that nurtured our dreams. What could we have accomplished if our parents were pushing us to follow our dreams from the moment we understood the concept? We are the first example to our children and usually their first hero. I take pride in being a positive example to my daughter. I speak life into her every chance I get because I want her to know there is nothing she can't do! Dreaming big is a household requirement.

When your child comes to you with a dream of theirs, no matter how silly it sounds, don't shut them down! Help them and guide them in any way you can. Your child's future will always be your best investment and it has the highest return. The return is emotionally healthy children who are not afraid to dream or take chances! As parents, it is not our job to tell them all the things they cannot do but to ensure that they know the many things they can! Affirm your child the same way you would affirm yourself! Tell them they are the greatest! You have to build their confidence from the early stages so they know there's nothing to fear!

Setting goals and planning for the future is not only for adults. When I started getting into planners, reading, and journaling, I had no idea it would be of interest to a kid. My daughter would ask me what I was doing and I'd explain it to her to the best of my abilities and also explain why I did it. Soon enough, she was asking for planners and journals and it became our bonding time! How cool is it to bond over your ambitions with your child?

Make dreaming fun! We would get some snacks, turn on some background music, and start with our gratitude journals. After we are done listing the things we are grateful for we'd plan out our week! Now she may have only had homework assignments, friends' birthdays, and chores to write in her planner, but it was more so about the habit I was creating in her. When I redecorated her room I installed a whiteboard on her wall. Sometimes I'd write a love message; other times I'd ask her to write a message to herself. You may have a child who hates writing in journals and reading; in that case switch it up to suit them but still try to stress the importance of dreaming big! Reassuring your child is one of the best things you can do for them.

Every child is different and no approach will work universally. I read The 5 Love Languages of Children by Gary Chapman and it helped me to really connect with my child in her love language. I recommend every parent read that book at least once. None of us has it all figured out when it comes to parenting but as long as we continue to make an honest effort our children will thank us!

What are some different things you can do with your children to encourage them to set goals as well as nurture their dreams?

You're not obligated to win.
You're obligated to
keep trying
to do the best you can
EVERYDAY

— MARIAN WRIGHT EDELMAN

Plan

Remember...
Procrastination is like masturbation,
In the beginning it *feels good,*

BUT IN THE END

you're just f***ing yourself!

— MICHAEL MCCARTHY

CHASE THOSE DREAMS!

A dream written down becomes a goal, a goal broken down into steps becomes a plan, backed by action makes

YOUR DREAMS
come true!

— UNKNOWN

Nothing is impossible
the word itself says
I'm POSSIBLE.
— AUDREY HEPBURN

My Dreams – The Timeline

Hopefully at this point, you have been able to identify your most pressing goals! Writing out your goals is just the initial phase, now let's plan out a course to help those goals come into fruition. When are you going to get started? When do you plan to have your goals accomplished? Take a look at your My Goals – The Breakdown Exercise and implement the goals you listed into a feasible timeline using the chart method shown on the next few pages.

Goal 1

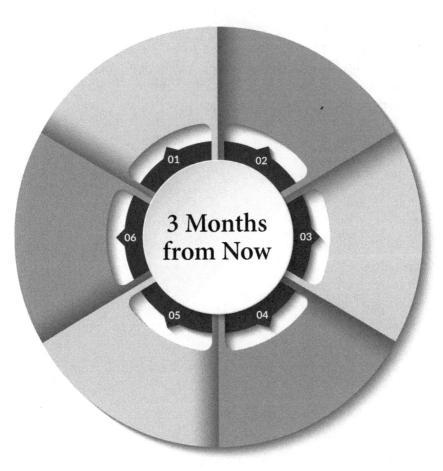

Goal 2

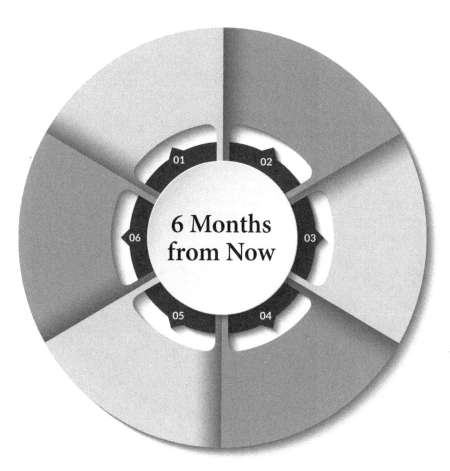

Goal 3

01
02
03
04
05
06

1 Year from Now

repeat after me

I am a money magnet. I welcome prosperity and abundance to overflow in my life.

never let anyone tell you

YOUR DREAMS

aren't realistic.
Their reality will
never be yours.

— CHIANA

Million-Dollar Dreams

It's time to stretch your dreams to the maximum! Remove those limitations off of yourself and dream with no limits. We all have a million dollars in our heads; we just need to find a way to get them out!

Remember in school when they would tell you "There is no such thing is a dumb question" or how about "The only dumb question is the one you didn't ask"? Well, use that same approach when it comes to your dreams! No dream is too big! The dream that you may think sounds the most ridiculous can turn out to be the most brilliant thing you've thought up!

If someone handed you a million dollars today, what would you do with it?

What businesses would you start?

What investments would you make?

Who would you help?

List out those million-dollar dreams and start believing you can make them come true, today!

_____

_____

_____

_____

_____

_____

_____

_____

_____

_____

_____

_____

_____

_____

_____

repeat after me

Multiple streams of income is a constant in my life.

when you feel copied,
remember people can
only go where
you have already been,
THEY HAVE NO IDEA
where you
are going next.

— LIZ LANGE

Execute

Just Get Started

Striving for perfection is the ultimate curse of growth. If you are waiting for things to be perfect in order to start, you will be waiting a lifetime.

Many people will never reach their full potential in life because they want everything to be perfect right out of the gate. Most times, just getting started will serve as one of your best teachers. You will have the opportunity to learn as you grow.

Take a look at one of your favorites, whether it's a business, a blogger, or celebrity. Go back and look at where they started and I guarantee you will be amazed. I can remember when I started my first blog. I drove myself nuts trying to make everything perfect to the eye. You know what happened? I was never satisfied, it was never good enough, and it didn't look PERFECT! I would stop working on it for weeks at a time trying to figure out how to piece together the ideal blog.

One day, I made a list of all the blogs I admire; it was time to do some research. I scrolled down each blog to read their very first post. This task helped me learn one very important lesson. Everyone had to start somewhere, and more than likely it wasn't at the top with the most elaborate website nor following. Yes, it takes time to build, but you will never see your dreams grow if you don't start laying the foundation.

I turned around and put my blog out there, without all of the elaborate photo shoots and expert writing skills. Surprisingly, I got a great response and I fell in love with the process.

Stop Operating in Fear! Just do that thing you've always dreamed of and make improvements along the way.

It's so common nowadays to see someone else succeed off of an idea you feel you came up with first. I know I've experienced it firsthand. I would sit around dreaming up all kinds of ideas but never acting on them. Fast-forward a couple of months, or even years, and sure enough someone else was able to make "my" dream happen.

What was I doing wrong? The only difference between them and me is that they acted on building their dreams while I waited for things to be perfect. Don't let another one of your dreams get taken from you. Get rid of your excuses and get rid of them right now! No, literally, right now!

Grab a sheet of paper and write out every excuse you have used to put off working toward your goals. Once you have that list, tear it to shreds, trash it, and never let those excuses leave your mouth again. Thank you. Instead of making excuses, learn to use the things working against you to your advantage.

If your dream is to start a business but you are not in a position to walk away from your job, plan it out anyway! Don't let anything kill your dreams. Use your time at work wisely. When you have downtime, do some research, or read an article pertaining to your interests. Log off of Facebook and make better use of your free time. Learn as much as you can from the company you're working at. How are they operating their business? What practices are they using that you could implement into your own strategy? Talk to people and perfect your communication skills. Once you stop thinking everything is working against you and use your disadvantages as a learning curve, you will look at your situation through a better light. Trust me, your life will improve just from removing negative feelings regarding your circumstances.

Furthermore, it takes money to make money. Your job is your first source of funding. Pay yourself something out of every single check and call it your "Dream Fund." Use that money ONLY to fund your dreams. I don't care if you can only pay yourself 10 dollars out of your check. Take that $10 and make it work. You can buy a domain name for $9.99! Everything doesn't have to be extreme. You have to keep moving. Slow progress is better than none at all.

Once you start acting on your dreams and putting your best foot forward, all of the other pieces will fall in place naturally.

repeat after me

Doors of opportunity are now open
for me to fulfill my dreams.

dreaming
doesn't cost you a
dime but the
HUSTLE
is sold separately
what are you
waiting for?

My Dreams – The Checklist

Each time you complete one of your goals, add it to the list below. It's important to keep track of your progress and to weigh in on how far you've come.

From Dream to Reality

☐ 1 _____

☐ 2 _____

☐ 3 _____

☐ 4 _____

☐ 5 _____

☐ 6 _____

☐ 7 _____

☐ 8 _____

☐ 9 _____

☐ 10 _____

Well Done

You've made it to the end, which means you've managed to get some serious work done.

Hopefully, by this point, you have been able to get clear and **DEFINE YOUR DREAMS!** I wish you well on your journey to success and self-discovery.

Continue to knock out your goals listed throughout this workbook one by one.

Remember to check in on your progress from time to time and refer back to these exercises as often as possible.

I'd love to see how you have made use of your workbook. Stay connected with me!

For more info, www.ChianaJenell.com

Instagram - @Chianajenell

Please include me on your journey!

Hashtag #ADREAMDEFINED so I can check out your progress!

NEVER QUIT YOUR DAYDREAM!

XO,

Chiana

Notes

Notes